FUN TO LEARN

Opposites

Words by Nina Filipeck
Illustrated by Jan Smith

book-studio

Jack and Jessie are friends but they like to do opposite things.

When Jack wants to play inside, where does Jessie want to play?

Jack and Jessie like playing at the playground.

Jack likes going down on the see-saw.

What does Jessie like doing?

When it is raining,
Jessie likes to be dry.

What does Jack like?

Jack and Jessie are on the beach with their buckets and shovels.

Jack's bucket is full.

Is there any sand in Jessie's bucket?

Jack and Jessie are painting a picture.

Jessie's hands are dirty.

Are Jack's hands dirty?

Jack and Jessie have different pet dogs.

Jack's dog has a long body.

Do you think Jessie's dog will be the same?

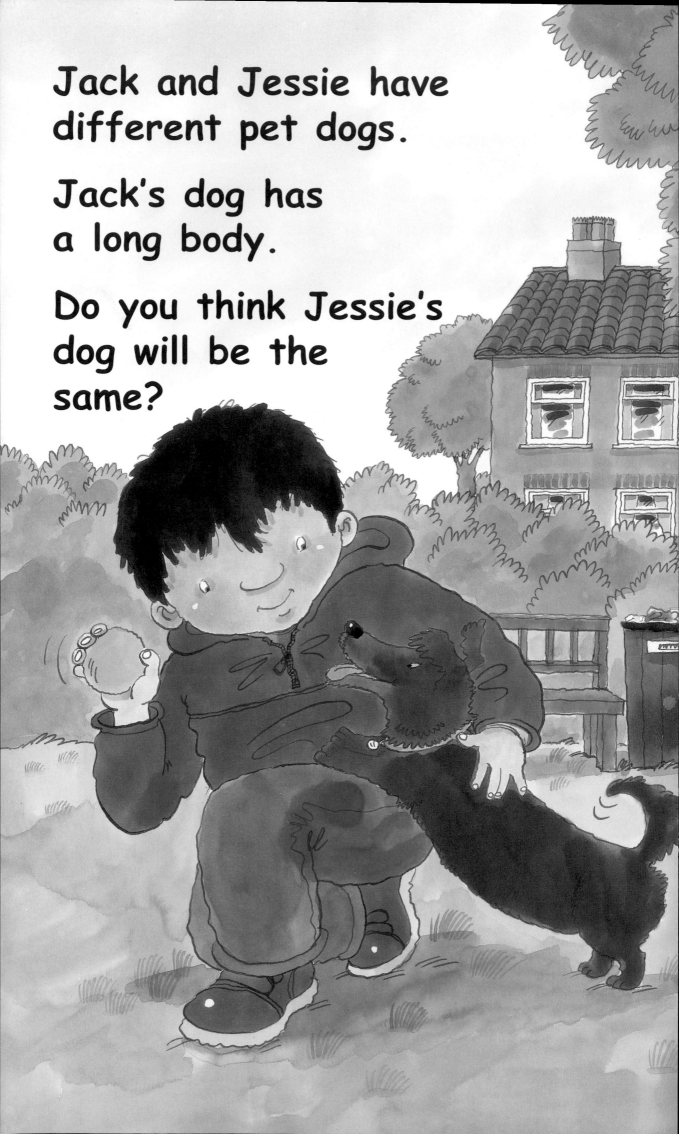

At mealtimes, the friends
have different drinks.

Jessie has a cold drink.

What drink does
Jack have?

When Jessie sleeps
over at Jack's house
they share a bunk bed.

Jack likes the
bottom bunk.

Which bunk
does Jessie like?

Goodnight Jack...
Goodnight Jessie.

The end

Jack and Jessie both love going to the zoo.

Jessie likes little animals.

Which animals does Jack like?